I HERO

Strike Force

Steve Barlow and Steve Skidmore
Illustrated by Sonia Leong

First published in 2009
by Franklin Watts

Cover design by Jonathan Hair

Franklin Watts
338 Euston Road
London NW1 3BH

A CIP catalogue record for this book
is available from the British Library.

ISBN: 978 0 7496 9036 6

3 5 7 9 10 8 6 4 2

Printed in Great Britain

Franklin Watts is a division of Hachette Children's Books,
an Hachette UK company.
www.hachette.co.uk

Decide your own destiny...

This book is not like others you may have read. *You* are the hero of this adventure. It is up to you to make decisions that will affect how the adventure unfolds.

Each section of this book is numbered. At the end of most sections, you will have to make a choice. The choice you make will take you to a different section of the book.

Some of your choices will help you to complete the adventure successfully. But choose carefully, some of your decisions could be fatal!

If you fail, then start the adventure again and learn from your mistake.

If you choose correctly you will succeed in your adventure.

Don't be a zero, be a hero!

You are a member of Strike Force, a Special Forces operations squad. You have taken part in many dangerous missions throughout the world. Strike Force agents are only called in as a last resort and you are on standby 24 hours, 7 days a week.

As a senior member of the force, you are a martial arts and weapons expert. You also speak many languages. One morning you are training in the Strike Force base gym, when a soldier enters and salutes. "Nemesis wishes to see you straight away. It's a Code Black," he says. You thank the soldier and head towards the top secret Strike Force operations centre. Nemesis is the codename for your boss, and Code Black is the highest mission level. Whatever task lies ahead for you, it is going to be very dangerous. You reach the operations centre and are directed to the secure briefing room. A guard opens the door and you enter. Sitting at a desk is your boss, Nemesis.

"We've got a situation," he says. "And we need you to deal with it."

Now turn to section 1.

1

Nemesis looks grimly at you. “We’ve no time to waste, so listen up. Victor Lokos, the President of the South American state of Amazonia is in Britain on an official state visit. His government has been very helpful in trying to destroy the drugs trade in his country.”

You nod. “I was on a mission there last year – Operation Greenleaf. It was a difficult mission; we nearly lost several operatives due to some bad intelligence given by our contact, Manos. My team had to sort out the mess. We located and destroyed a drugs factory in the Amazon forest and arrested several gang members. No thanks to Manos.”

Nemesis' voice is hard. "Operation Greenleaf didn't go down well with the drug barons. They swore revenge and it seems that they have lived up to their promise. We have a Code Black situation and I need you. However, it will mean that you will have to work with Manos again. I wouldn't ask you to do this if it wasn't important." You consider carefully. Manos nearly caused Operation Greenleaf to fail, but this sounds like an important mission.

If you decide that you don't want to work with Manos, go to 35.

If you agree to work with Manos, go to 12.

2

"We have to stop the van," you tell Manos.

"How will we do that?" he asks. You have to make a quick decision.

If you want the helicopter to force the van off the road, go to 44.

If you want to attempt to drop onto the roof of the van, go to 19.

If you decide to shoot at the van's tyres, go to 41.

3

You put your foot down on the accelerator and speed through the country lanes. The sporty SUV screeches around corners, narrowly missing other vehicles.

The sat phone rings again. It is Nemesis. "You're too late," he says. "The girl has been kidnapped. The President is furious. He doesn't want you anywhere near the operation to rescue his granddaughter. I'll send in another team. Return to base."

You have failed. If you wish to begin your mission again, turn to 1.

4

You sling the machine-gun over your shoulder and step to the door's edge.

"Ten metre drop, go!" you shout at Manos. He releases the winch brake and you leap out backwards. You plunge downwards for ten metres and then the rope yanks tight. You are now dangling above the roof of the van, travelling fast. You glance ahead and see some electricity pylons. There are cables spanning the road. In less than thirty seconds you will hit them. You have to react immediately!

If you want to order Manos to winch you back up immediately, go to 20.

If you wish to shoot at the van, go to 26.

If you want to try to attach the tracking bug to the van's roof, go to 36.

5

As the van heads towards the helicopter, you shout at the pilot to fly higher.

He does so just in time. The roof of the van brushes the undercarriage of the helicopter as it accelerates down the road. "Keep the van in sight," you order. The helicopter and van chase along the road at high speed.

If you want to attempt to drop onto the roof of the van, go to 19.

If you decide to shoot at the van's tyres, go to 41.

6

"How do you know all this?" you ask.

"I have an informer in the gang," Manos replies. "His codename is Puma. He has told me that a kidnap attempt is going to happen very soon."

"And is this information reliable?" you ask.

"I would trust Puma with my life."

"It might not be your life that is on the line," you tell Manos. "It might be mine..."

Go to 18.

7

As you swing wildly on the rope, you shoot at the van, but miss your target.

The electricity cables are getting nearer. You signal Manos to winch you up.

Go to 17.

8

You order the helicopter pilot to slow down.

Eventually you reach the school and the helicopter lands. The other military units have already arrived, but they are too late. Several policemen are dead and the kidnappers have taken the girl. You radio Nemesis and tell him what has happened. He is furious. "You slowed down! What sort of agent are you! Don't bother coming back to base! You are finished in Strike Force, you coward!" Someone else will have to try and rescue the girl.

If you wish to start your mission again, go to 1.

9

"Manos is right," you say. "We should take the Strike Force helicopter. It's loaded with weapons and equipment, and ready for takeoff at five minutes notice."

Nemesis nods in agreement. "Very well. Get to the school and bring back the girl before the gang get to her. Your Code Black orders are not to return without her. Understood? Good luck."

Go to 46.

10

The van continues to speed along the country lanes. Although the helicopter pilot does his best, it is getting more difficult to follow it. It won't be long before it gets away.

If you want the helicopter to force the van off the road, go to 44.

If you want to attempt to drop onto the roof of the van, go to 19.

11

"Keep following the target," you tell the pilot. "But don't get too close, we want them to think they've lost us."

Using the tracking device, you follow the van for some time. Finally the van stops. You circle around before flying nearer. The van is parked in a disused industrial estate, outside a warehouse. You radio the location to Strike Force base. Nemesis tells you that other units are half an hour away. "That's too long," you say. "The gang are nervous – they could kill the girl and try to escape. We need to go in now and surprise them."

If you want to land and search on foot, go to 33.

If you want to search the warehouse using the helicopter's heat-detecting equipment, go to 37.

12

You realise that you have to trust Nemesis's judgement. "If you say it is important, I'll work with him."

"Thank you." Nemesis smiles and presses an intercom button. "Send Manos in." The door opens and Manos enters. "You two know each other," says Nemesis. You glare at Manos. He steps forward and holds out his hand.

If you wish to shake his hand, go to 25.
If you wish to ignore his greeting, go to 43.

13

Before you can ready your weapon and fire, you see a gun pointing at you.

A volley of shots ring out. Pain rips through your body and blackness engulfs you. Your failure has cost you your life.

If you wish to begin the mission again, go to 1.

14

You order the pilot to circle as the gang bundle the girl into their van. As they make their getaway, you tell the pilot to follow the van. You radio Nemesis and ask him to tell the other units to track the Strike Force helicopter.

The chase continues and it begins to get dark. You switch on the helicopter's searchlight. The van speeds along country lanes and it gets harder to keep it in sight.

If you wish to continue the chase, go to 10.

If you decide that you need to try to make the van stop, go to 2.

15

As you stand up, you see a man moving behind a stack of boxes, ten metres to your left. He obviously hasn't seen you.

You dive to the floor and crawl towards the boxes. You get nearer and nearer. As you are about to leap up and open fire, you hear a girl crying. You realise that the granddaughter is also behind the boxes. You can't begin shooting, you might hit her. You move quickly across the ground. In an instant you are behind the stack of boxes and you point your gun at the gang member. He throws up his hands and cries out, "Don't shoot, I am Puma!"

If you want to ignore him and open fire, go to 13.

If you wish to listen to what he has to say, go to 34.

16

The lights of the van are blinding. "Stay here!" you order the pilot.

Just as it seems as though the van is going to crash into the helicopter, it swerves away. There is a terrible screeching noise as the van tips over and rolls towards the trees at the side of the road. You look on in horror as the van smashes into a tree and bursts into flames. You leap out of the helicopter, but it is too late, everyone in the van is dead. You have killed the President's granddaughter – you have failed.

If you wish to begin your mission again, go to 1.

17

Manos switches on the winch and you fly upwards.

The cables are almost upon you. The pilot pulls the helicopter up and misses them by centimetres, but for you it is too late. Dangling helplessly, you spin into the cables. Sparks light up the sky and you scream in agony as the deadly electricity brings your mission to an end.

If you wish to begin your adventure again, go back to 1.

18

You turn to Nemesis. "So what do you need me for?" you ask. "Surely it is a police job to protect the girl?"

"The President asked for you personally. He wants you to guard his granddaughter. He thinks highly of you because of the work you did on Operation Greenleaf. In the meantime, an armed police unit has been sent to the school to make sure she is safe until you arrive. Bring back the girl so we can protect her until we discover who the kidnappers are."

"I will accompany you," says Manos.

You are not happy about this. "Is that necessary?" you ask.

"Yes, and that's an order..." replies Nemesis.

If you agree to let Manos accompany you, go to 39.

If you want to disobey Nemesis's order, go to 49.

19

"I'm going to abseil down onto the roof. You operate the winch," you say to Manos.

You put on a harness and attach the winch rope to a metal clip. A gust of wind hits you in the face as you open the door. You tell the helicopter pilot to fly directly over the roof of the van. You put on your night-vision goggles. You reach into the Strike Force equipment box and pick up a magnetic tracking bug. But which weapon should you take?

If you decide to sling a machine-gun over your shoulder, go to 4.

If you would prefer to take a handgun, go to 28.

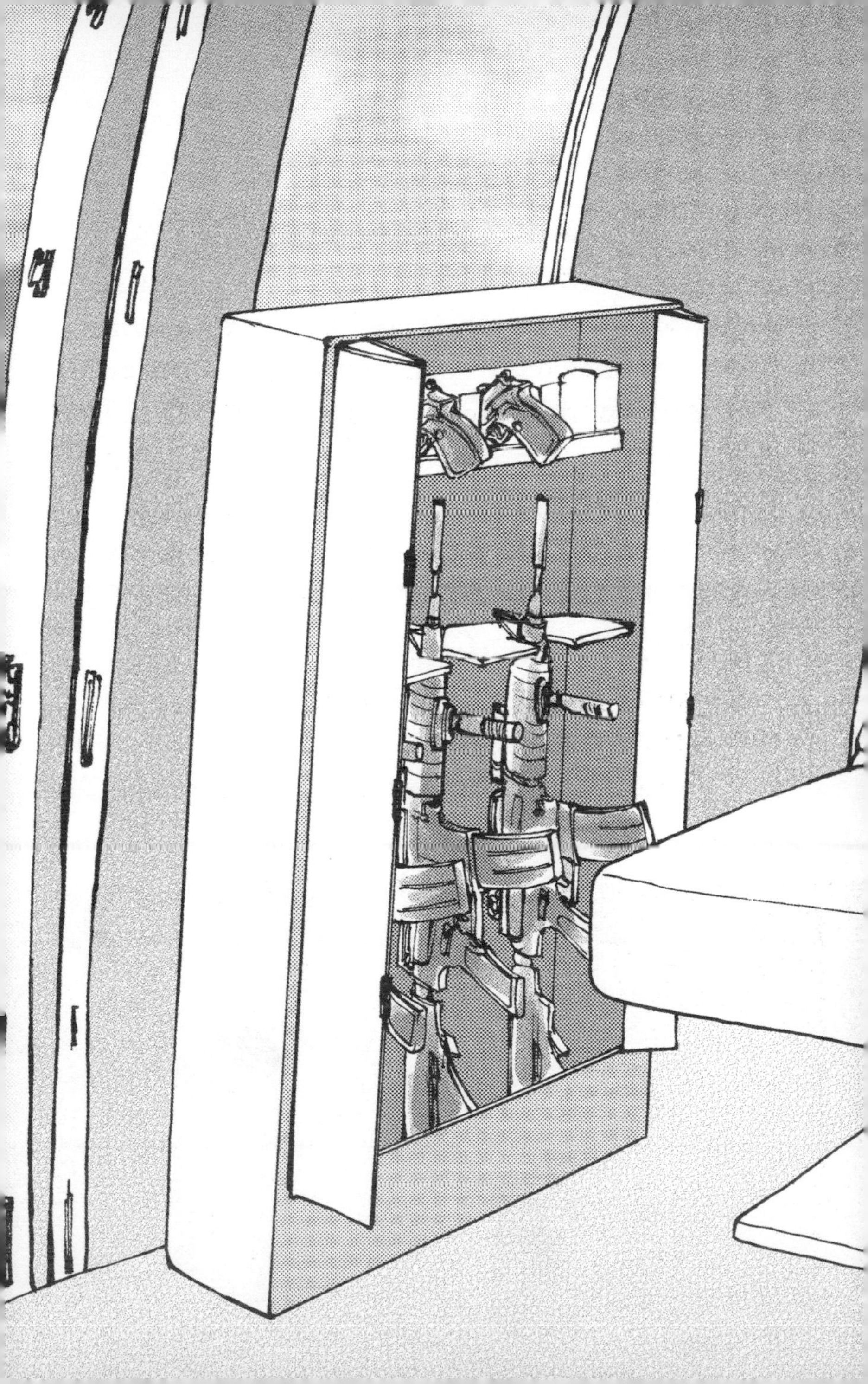

20

You order Manos to winch you back up.

The electricity cables get nearer and nearer as you are pulled upwards. The pilot pulls hard on the controls and the helicopter easily misses the cables. The helicopter swings around and you search below for the van. You fly around in vain, looking for the van. You have lost it. You radio Nemesis. He is furious. "I'll let the other units deal with this. Return to base."

You have failed. If you wish to begin again, go to 1.

21

"You're worrying too much," you tell Manos. "The kidnappers won't strike yet. We'll take the SUV."

"Keep in contact on your journey and good luck," says Nemesis.

You leave the room with Manos and head over to the Strike Force vehicle compound. The SUV is loaded with Strike Force weapons and equipment. "Get in," you tell Manos. He does so. You programme the sat nav system and set off.

You have been driving for 15 minutes, when your sat phone rings. It is Nemesis. "We have reports of armed attackers at the school. You need to get there immediately!"

If you wish to drive as fast as possible to the school, go to 3.

If you wish to return to the base and take the helicopter, go to 31.

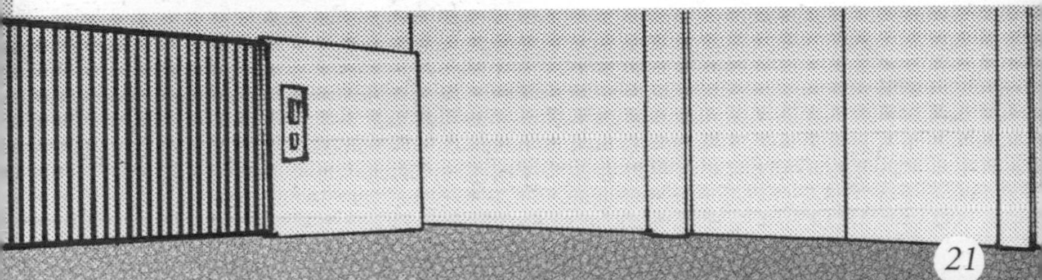

22

You pick up Helena and carefully make your way back with Puma to Manos.

You tell Puma to help Manos outside and radio your helicopter to come and pick you up. Seconds later, you see several other helicopters flying low. Ropes are flung out and squads of soldiers abseil down and rush towards the warehouse. You smile, knowing that the surviving members of the gang will soon be dealt with. You and Puma lift Helena and Manos into the helicopter before climbing in yourselves. "Let's go home," you tell the pilot.

Go to 50.

23

You order the pilot to increase speed. Soon the helicopter is hovering over the school.

You radio Nemesis and he tells you that there are reports of police casualties. The gang have already seized the President's granddaughter and are heading towards their escape vehicle at the rear of the school. You pick up your machine-gun and order the pilot to fly to the rear of the school. You see a group of men heading towards a van. You can see that they are dragging a young girl with them. Police are following, but not firing. What should you do?

If you choose to fly in and shoot at the gang members, go to 38.

If you decide to land the helicopter near the escape vehicle, go to 33.

If you would rather let the gang get into their van and follow it in the helicopter, go to 14.

POLICE
POLICE

24

You take a combat knife from your belt and cut the rope.

You drop onto the van's roof with a thump. The van accelerates forward and you nearly slide off. Somehow you manage to keep your balance and attach the tracking bug to the roof. Having done what you needed to do, you brace yourself and leap off the roof. You hit the road and roll over and over.

Go to 27.

25

For the sake of the mission, you shake Manos's hand.

"I am sorry for what happened in Operation Greenleaf," Manos says. "I give you my word that I will make no mistakes this time."

You are still wary of Manos, but accept his apology. "Very well. So what is this all about?" you ask. Manos hands you a file. You open it and see a picture of a young girl. Manos begins his briefing.

"This is Helena Lokos, the President's granddaughter. For the past year she has secretly been a pupil in Britain at a boarding school called Bearham Park. No one knows her true identity. However, on his visit to Britain, the President said he wanted to visit Helena. This has led to a security breach. Helena's true identity and her location are now in the open. I have had information that the drug barons intend to kidnap her. They will then kill her if the President doesn't release all gang members captured in Operation Greenleaf." You need to know more information about the mission. Who should you ask?

If you wish to direct your questions to Nemesis, go to 18.

If you wish to ask Manos, go to 6.

26

You try to take the machine-gun from your shoulder, but on the swinging rope you struggle to reach it. You're taking too long! Through your night-vision goggles you see a figure shooting at you from the van. Bullets rip into you. Your lifeless body hangs from the rope.

You have failed completely. If you wish to start again, turn back to 1.

27

The van speeds away as you stand up and brush yourself down. You speak into your radio. "Pick me up."

Minutes later the helicopter has landed and you climb inside. "Well done," says Manos. You switch on the tracking system and breathe a sigh of relief. The tracker is working. What is your plan of action?

If you wish to return to base and let other units deal with the situation, go to 45.

If you decide to follow the van, go to 11.

28

You pick up the handgun and step to the door's edge.

"Ten metre drop, go!" you tell Manos. He releases the winch brake and you leap out backwards. You plunge downwards for ten metres and then the rope yanks tight. You are now dangling above the roof of the van, travelling fast. You glance ahead and see some electricity pylons. There are cables spanning the road. In less than thirty seconds you will hit them. You have to react immediately!

If you want to try to attach the tracking bug, go to 36.

If you want to order Manos to winch you back up immediately, go to 20.

If you wish to stay where you are and shoot at the van, go to 7.

29

"Let me see the injury."

As you bend forward, Manos brings his gun up and points it at you. You stare in horror and brace yourself for the impact. He pulls the trigger and a stream of bullets fly over your shoulder. There is a cry from behind you and you spin around to see a gang member falling to the floor. You realise that Manos has saved your life. "Thanks," you say.

"See, I can be trusted," replies Manos, "Now leave me and get the girl!"

Go to 15.

30

"Lower me five metres," you shout into your radio.

Manos obeys and you drop onto the roof of the van with a thump. As you do, the van accelerates forward. You fix the tracking bug onto the roof of the van. The cables are getting closer. How will you get off the roof?

If you decide to cut your rope, go to 40.

If you want to order Manos to winch you back up, go to 17.

31

You swing on the wheel of the car and spin it around. You put your foot down on the accelerator and speed along the country lanes.

The car screeches around corners, narrowly missing other vehicles. You radio ahead and tell them to get the helicopter ready for immediate takeoff. Your expert driving gets you back to the base in record time. You slide the car to a halt, jump out and head to the Strike Force helicopter. Manos follows.

Go to 46.

32

You take aim and let go of the tracking bug. As you do, the van accelerates forward. The bug hits the side of the roof and bounces onto the ground. You curse. There is no time to try to place another tracker.

Go to 20.

33

You order the pilot to land the helicopter near the gang's van.

As he does so, the gang open fire. Moving so slowly, the helicopter is a sitting target! You return fire and shout, "Pull away!"

It is too late. A stream of bullets rips through the helicopter. You feel a searing pain in your chest and drop to the floor. You have paid the ultimate price.

If you wish to begin your mission again, return to 1.

34

"Are you Manos's contact?" you ask.

"Yes," he answers and slowly moves aside to reveal the President's granddaughter. "I moved her away from the rest of the gang when your attack began. We need to get her away from the others that are left. They will surely kill her as a punishment." You nod in agreement and hold out your hand.

"Come with me, Helena. You're going to be safe." Still trembling, she takes hold of your hand.

Go to 22.

35

"I'm afraid I don't want to work with him," you say. "I can't trust him."

Nemesis is not impressed. "I could order you to do this. And if you refuse…"

What should you do?

If you agree to work with Manos, go to 12.
If you still don't want to, go to 49.

36

You take the tracking bug from your pocket and flick the switch to activate it.

It is magnetic and will stick to the roof. You are five metres above the roof and the cables are getting nearer. How will you attach the tracking bug to the roof?

If you want to drop it onto the roof and hope it sticks, go to 32.

If you wish to order Manos to lower you onto the roof, and then attach it, go to 30.

If you wish to cut your rope and drop onto the roof, go to 24.

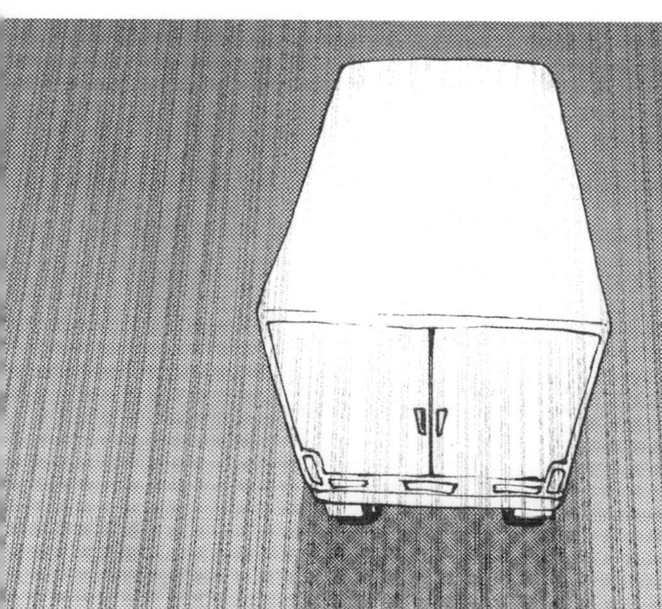

37

You order the pilot to fly around, whilst you check out the warehouse. The heat-detecting equipment helps you to pinpoint the gang. They are on the ground floor, near the front of the building.

You can make out six figures. You guess that one of these must be the President's granddaughter, leaving five gang members. You like the odds. How should you attack the warehouse?

If you wish to make a full-frontal attack, go to 33.

If you wish to attack the rear of the building, go to 48.

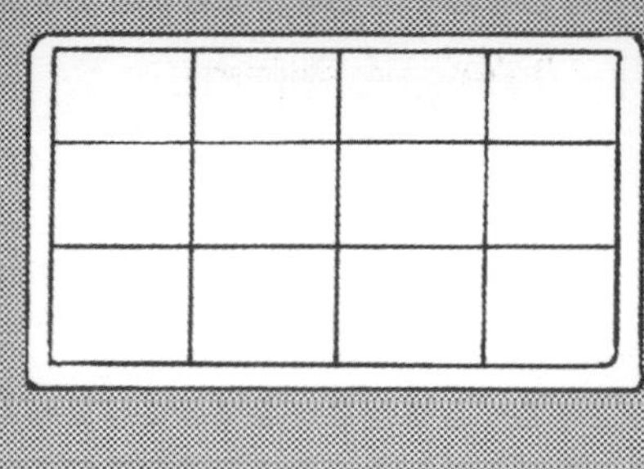

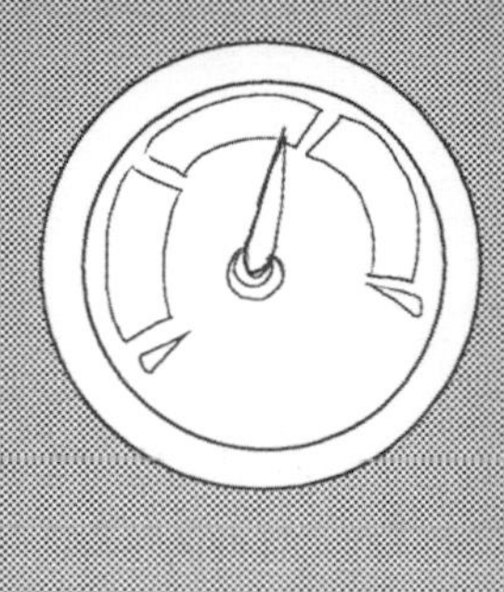
25°C
34°C
22°C
090313 05:06:08
e=0.95

38

As you take aim, Manos grabs hold of your arm. "You can't risk it! You might hit the girl!" You pause. Is Manos right? Should you choose another option?

If you wish to ignore Manos, go to 47.

If you decide to land the helicopter near the escape vehicle, go to 33.

If you would rather let the gang get into their van and follow it in the helicopter, go to 14.

39

"Very well," you say. "How far is the school from here?"

"Two hours by road," says Nemesis. "You could take a Strike Force SUV."

"Two hours is a long time," says Manos. "We could be too late."

If you agree with Manos, go to 9.
If you disagree with him, go to 21.

40

You take a knife from your belt and cut your rope. The helicopter pulls away.

Having done what you needed to do, you brace yourself and leap off the roof. You hit the road and roll over and over.

Go to 27.

41

You open the helicopter's door.

You pick up your gun, take aim at the van's tyres and pull the trigger. Your gun kicks back and a stream of bullets light up the sky. The van driver swerves in order to avoid the attack as you continue to fire at the vehicle. Suddenly, the tyres of the van burst. The vehicle lurches across the road. You watch in horror as it spins wildly across the road and hits a tree. There is an explosion and the van is engulfed in flames.

"You fool!" cries Manos. "You've killed the President's granddaughter."

You have failed in you mission. If you wish to begin again, go to 1.

42

You throw a stun grenade. The air is full of noise and smoke. You move forward carefully, looking for the girl.

Suddenly there is a burst of fire from your right and Manos is hit. You spin round and return fire. The man who shot Manos drops to the ground. You rush to Manos and kneel over him. "I'm all right," he says. "It's just my leg. You go on."

If you want to deal with Manos's injury, go to 29.

If you want to continue your hunt for the girl, go to 15.

43

You stand facing Manos. "Your bad intelligence nearly cost my team's lives," you say.

"I am sorry you feel like that," replies Manos. "I can assure you I was acting in good faith. Will you forgive me?" You remain silent.

"We need his help, so I am ordering you to accept his apology," says Nemesis.

If you wish to obey Nemesis, go to 25.

If you don't, go to 49.

44

You tell the pilot to fly over the van. He accelerates past the vehicle at top speed.

You are four hundred metres ahead of the van, when you tell him to turn the helicopter round and hover just above the road. He does so. The van's headlights shine brightly as it speeds towards you. It is not slowing down!

If you wish to shoot at the van, go to 41.

If you decide to order the pilot to fly higher, go to 5.

If you decide to keep the helicopter in position, go to 16.

45

You return to the Strike Force base and head to the operations centre. Nemesis is amazed to see you.

"Where is the girl?" he asks. You tell him what happened. He is furious. "I gave you a Code Black order not to return without her!" You try to explain, but he will not listen to you. "But the girl is not here!" he growls.

Go to 49.

46

You climb into the helicopter, put on your communication device and order the pilot to head to the school at top speed.

As the helicopter skims over the treetops, you radio Nemesis for an update. He tells you that the gang have seized the girl and are currently engaged in a shoot-out with armed police. Other military units have been sent to the school, but will not reach it before you do.

If you decide to wait for these units to arrive, go to 8.

If you wish to get to the school as quickly as possible, go to 23.

47

You shrug away Manos's protests and pull the trigger. Bullets rain down on the gang. They return fire. As the battle continues, you see the girl drop to the floor. You've hit her!

"You fool!" screams Manos. "What have you done?" The gang continues to fire at the helicopter. It takes a direct hit to the rotors and you plunge to the ground.

You have failed completely. If you wish to start again, turn back to 1.

48

You tell the pilot to land the helicopter away from the warehouse. As he does, you and Manos arm yourselves and put on gas masks and helmets.

The helicopter comes to a halt and you tell the pilot to begin a frontal attack on the warehouse on your command. You leap out with Manos and head for the rear of the warehouse. There is a shutter door, which is locked. You place an explosive device against it and then use your radio to order the helicopter pilot to make an attack on the front of the building. You hear the helicopter zooming in, guns blazing. You hit the detonator and the door explodes. You rush in.

If you decide to throw stun grenades, go to 42.
If you wish to begin shooting, go to 13.

49

"No," you say, grimly.

"Then get out!" shouts Nemesis. "As a member of Strike Force, you know that disobeying an order means it is the end of your career!" You leave. Your career in Strike Force is over.

If you wish to begin the adventure again, return to 1.

50

Some days later you are called into the Strike Force operations centre. Nemesis sits at his desk.

"What mission is it now?" you ask.

"Nothing for the moment. There's someone who wanted to see you."

The door opens and Manos limps in. You nod towards his leg. "Just a scratch," he smiles. "My president wishes to thank you for the great service you did."

"Just doing my job," you reply. "While there are bad people out there, Strike Force has to be ready to deal with them."

He nods. "Puma and I are moving into other fields of intelligence, but perhaps we will meet again."

"Perhaps we will," you say. "I look forward to it." You hold out your hand. He takes it and gives you a firm handshake.

"Thank you again, you are a real hero!"

I HERO

All these I, Hero titles are available now!

978 0 7496 9036 6

978 0 7496 8264 4

978 0 7496 8265 1

978 0 7496 7667 4

978 0 7496 7664 3

978 0 7496 7666 7

978 0 7496 7665 0

Space Rescue

Steve Barlow and Steve Skidmore

Illustrated by Sonia Leong

You are the top astronaut at UNSA (United Nations Space Agency). You have flown into space many times. You are the one that UNSA calls if there is an emergency.

Early one morning, you are woken by the buzz of your Satvid phone.

"Answer," you say. The video screen flicks on to reveal a worried-looking man.

"We have a Red Alert," he says. "We need you at UNSA HQ immediately. An Agency car is on its way."

"Okay," you reply. "I'll get my things."

You wonder what danger this new mission will bring.

I HERO

DECIDE YOUR OWN DESTINY

Space Rescue

Steve Barlow - Steve Skidmore